SCHOOL
THE AWFUL TRUTH

Scoular Anderson

Hodder
Children's
Books

a division of Hodder Headline plc

For the staff and pupils of
Innellan Primary School
who SPLAT! *helped with this book.*

Text and illustrations copyright 1999 © Scoular Anderson
Published by Hodder Children's Books 1999

Book design by Joy Mutter
Cover illustration by Scoular Anderson

The right of Scoular Anderson to be identified as the author and illustrator of the work has been asserted by him in accordance with the Copyright, Designs and Patents Act 1988.

10 9 8 7 6 5 4 3

A catalogue record for this book is available from the British Library.

ISBN: 0 340 73615 1

Printed and bound by the Guernsey Press Co. Ltd,
Guernsey, Channel Islands.

Hodder Children's Books
a division of Hodder Headline plc
338 Euston Road
London NW1 3BH

CONTENTS

Schools come in all shapes and sizes. Here are
five of the most common ones:

THE BATS IN THE BELFRY SCHOOL.
OLD ENOUGH TO HAVE WOODWORM AND GHOSTS.

GRRR

THE ONE-THOUSAND-AND-ONE-STAIRS SCHOOL.
THE PUPILS ON THE TOP FLOOR ARE THE FITTEST BUT
ALSO THE SLEEPIEST AS THEY HAVE TO WALK FURTHEST.

THE GULLS-ON-THE-ROOF-(PLUS-OLD FOOTBALLS-AND-EVEN-SHOES) SCHOOL.

THE-MILLION-MILE-LONG-CORRIDOR SCHOOL. PUPILS ARE ALLOWED TO EAT SNACKS TO GIVE THEM ENERGY TO WALK FROM ONE END TO THE OTHER.

MOST SCHOOLS HAVE A LARGE PET THE SIZE OF AN ELEPHANT IN THE PLAYGROUND. IT'S CALLED A PORTACABIN.

Good old girl!

GRRR

7

Teachers come in all shapes and sizes, too. Here are a few examples.

Do any of these look like *your* teacher?

If not, these pictures can be rearranged in a computer to get a new set of teachers.

Perhaps one of these looks like your teacher.

But never mind the shape of the building or the teacher. What *really* goes on in school? To find out we're going to sent a spy into school. She's called . . .

SQUEAK...
...SQUEAK..!

GOOD...MOR...NING...PU...PILS!

Her name is Mrs Meggabight.

Mrs Meggabight has visited a school near you.

She has left no jotter unopened.

She has left no bit of gunge unprodded.

She has left no waste-paper bin unrummaged.

She has left no plate of Spaghetti Bolognese (with extra cheesy sauce) (no matter how old) untasted . . .

So she has been able to find out the AWFUL TRUTH about school.

MEGGABIGHT REPORT ON......

THE AWFUL TRUTH ABOUT THE THING IN THE SINK

Mrs Meggabight is about to give her first report. She's discovered a really awful fact . . .

PRINTING: PAGE 1

BRRRRR!

CLICK! CLICK!

Every school has The Thinginthesink. It lives down in the dark, slimy, sticky bit beneath the plug hole. Sometimes it makes strange noises.

Sometimes The Thinginthesink makes a terrible smell. It can knock you out at six paces.

A lot of the time the pupils feed The Thinginthesink.

WARNING:
YOU SHOULD *NEVER* FEED THE THINGINTHESINK

The more you feed it, the more it wants.
Sometimes it will come out of its den with a hungry look on its face.

First, it lies in the bottom of the sink. It's usually a greyish-brownish-purplish-greenish colour.

If no one gives it a snack you will see its many long legs as it tries to climb out of the sink.

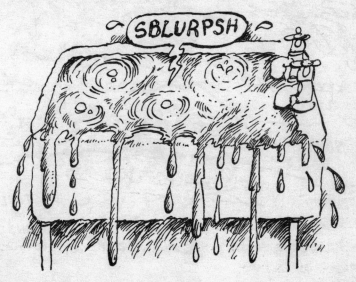

If it crawls across the floor you can see the things that pupils have been feeding it.

PAINT BRUSHES

LOUISE'S HOUSE KEY

KEVIN'S TOOTH

SOMETHING NASTY

RED PAINT

SPIDER'S LEG

ELASTOPLAST FROM KEVIN'S BOIL

But help is at hand! In a flash, Super-Thinginthesink-Buster arrives, also known as . . .

PAPER TOWELS

PLASTIC DINOSAUR

GLASS EYE (TEDDY BEAR)

BIT OF CHRISTMAS TINSEL

PIECE OF STRING

SLUG

CHEWING GUM

NEWT

PIECE OF HAM

The school caretaker or janitor. (COJ for short.)
The COJ at the school near you is called
Mr Glaggum.

THE AWFUL TRUTH ABOUT THE SCHOOL CARETAKER OR JANITOR (COJ)

The COJ usually lives in a little room near the school's main door. Mrs Meggabight managed to get Mr Glaggum out of his little room and away to the other end of the school. She was able to get into his little room and give it a thorough inspection.

This is what Mrs Meggabight found . . .

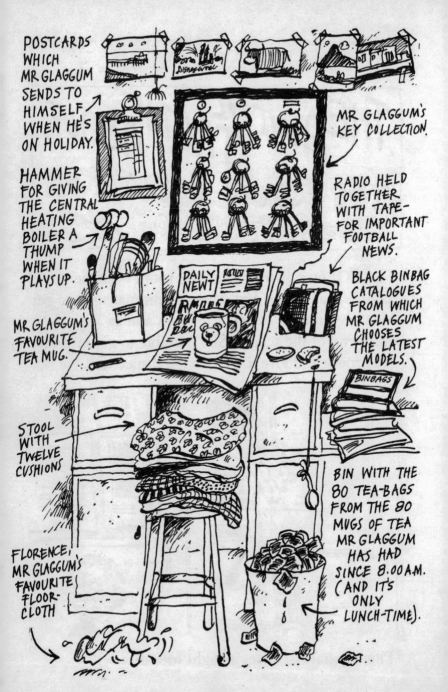

POSTCARDS WHICH MR GLAGGUM SENDS TO HIMSELF WHEN HE'S ON HOLIDAY.

MR GLAGGUM'S KEY COLLECTION.

HAMMER FOR GIVING THE CENTRAL HEATING BOILER A THUMP WHEN IT PLAYS UP.

RADIO HELD TOGETHER WITH TAPE-FOR IMPORTANT FOOTBALL NEWS.

MR GLAGGUM'S FAVOURITE TEA MUG.

BLACK BINBAG CATALOGUES FROM WHICH MR GLAGGUM CHOOSES THE LATEST MODELS.

BINBAGS

STOOL WITH TWELVE CUSHIONS

BIN WITH THE 80 TEA-BAGS FROM THE 80 MUGS OF TEA MR GLAGGUM HAS HAD SINCE 8.00 A.M. (AND IT'S ONLY LUNCH-TIME).

FLORENCE, MR GLAGGUM'S FAVOURITE FLOOR-CLOTH

DAILY NEWT

20

Mrs Meggabight advises you to keep your COJ happy at all times. For instance, the pupils keep in Mr Glaggum's good books by . . .

A: Telling him really funny jokes.

B: Offering him some of their sweets and crisps.

Because the AWFUL TRUTH about COJs is . . .

they are ALIENS.
They can suddenly turn VERY NASTY.

Here are some of the things that turn Mr Glaggum into a dangerous alien:

Pupils dropping bits of litter on the floor, no matter how small.

Things pupils bring in on their shoes, like chewing gum, mud, dog poo etc.

Other messy things that pupils leave on the floor.

Football marks on the windows.

Footballs (or shoes, sandwiches, pens etc.) on the roofs or gutters.

However, Mr Glaggum has a storeroom full of equipment to deal with these things.

NEW MOP FOR VERY SPECIAL OCCASIONS

OLD SMELLY MOP

REALLY ANCIENT SMELLY MOP (PROBABLY MADE OF DINOSAUR SKIN)

FLORENCE THE FLOORCLOTH

SPONGE (BOUGHT IN 2,005 B.C.)

PLUNGER FOR CLEARING DRAINS, REMOVING PUPILS, ETC.

AIR FRESHNER WHICH MR GLAGGUM SPRAYS OVER EVERYTHING.

PHHT!

YEUCH!

Remember: don't mess with the COJ and don't make a mess.

MEGGABIGHT REPORT ON...
THE AWFUL TRUTH ABOUT NOISE

Mrs Meggabight is putting out her special sensors. She's going to find out how noisy schools are.

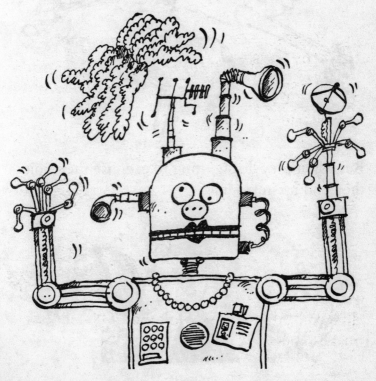

Mrs Meggabight has noticed a strange fact. In school pupils do sums to exercise their brains.

They do PE to exercise their bodies.

But when they do shouting to exercise their voices they end up in trouble.

Teachers usually start doing their snake impressions.

Mrs Meggabight has been all round the school near you. Here are some of the noises her special sensors picked up:

The Teacher Trumpet

Teachers often try to make a louder noise than their pupils.

The Swingdoor Drums

Schools have lots of doors. many of them think they are musicians. They sing in an awful squeaky voice and accompany themselves on drums.

The Photocopier Fanfare

Every school has a machine like this. Often it sits in the middle of a corridor. It makes a whole range of noises, like a weird orchestra.

The Dinner Lady Din

The noise comes from behind the kitchen shutters just before lunch time.

The Seccy Snap Rap

The school secretary usually wears loud shoes. As she walks around her shoes beat out a jazzy rhythm like a pair of crazy castanets.

And now the noisiest noise of all:

The Fire-bell Freak-out

At a school near you the fire-bell sometimes goes off by accident because . . .
The dinner ladies have burnt the curry . . .

. . . or Javed has left his wet gloves and socks on a radiator.

As soon as the fire-alarm gets a whiff of these sorts of things, it goes berserk . . .

Miss Teylfeather then does her rocket-to-the-moon impression.

Just to add even more excitement (and noise), the fire brigade arrives.

The AWFUL TRUTH about schools is that they are the noisiest places on earth, maybe even in the universe.

MEGGABIGHT REPORT ON...

THE AWFUL TRUTH ABOUT ART

Mrs Meggabight has been looking at the materials that pupils use in art. There are a lot of art jokes.

The Pointless Pencil Joke

Pencils work best when they're nice and sharp . . .

. . . but just blink once . . .

. . . and the pencil point disappears. Now you need a sharpener.

The Starving Sharpener Joke

Sharpeners have a huge appetite. Their little mouths are always wide open. Put a nice new pencil in the mouth and in a split second it will chew it down to a stump.

The Slipping Scissors Joke

Using scissors is like
taking the dog for a
walk. Take your eye
off them for a moment
and they'll stray off
and do something you
don't want them to do.

The Wandering Wax Crayon Joke

Wax crayons are very
disobedient. No matter
how stern you are with
them, they will still
wander all over
the place.

The Fuzzy Felt Pen Joke

The colour you want has
always run out or the nib
looks as fuzzy as a
badger's ear.

But now for the biggest jokers of all.
The dreadful duo:

THE GUNGY GLUEPOT

AND THE PAINTY SPONGE (OR SPUDGE)

SPLURP!

Mrs Meggabight has been watching the GluePot and the Painty Sponge (or spudge) in action. Miss Teylfeather was making a wall frieze with her pupils.

Firstly, the pupils were going to make an interesting background with sponges dipped in paint.

Next, the pupils painted a ship, oars, masts, sails, shields, Vikings etc. to stick on the painted background.

The AWFUL TRUTH about art is that pencils, crayons, glue, paint have a *very* strange sense of humour. They never do what they're supposed to do.

Instead of gluing or painting pictures, pupils usually paint the furniture, the floor, themselves etc.

THE AWFUL TRUTH ABOUT "EXERCISE"

Many people think that PE stands for *Physical Education*. The AWFUL TRUTH is that PE really stands for *Pupil Elastication*. It's the PE teacher's job to make the pupils bodies as elastic and bendy as possible.

Mrs Meggabight has put on her tracksuit and crash helmet. She's going to join the children for PE.

Here are some of the exercises the pupils had to do to make themselves elastic.

The hulahoops are supposed to exercise the hips but they usually tangle the legs.

Sometimes the hoops are laid on the floor. Pupils have to jump from one hoop to the other without touching the floor in between (or they get eaten by sharks). Sometimes the teacher will move a hoop so that pupils have to stretch their legs.

Running round and round and round and round
and round the hall is a good exercise for heart
and lungs. Sometimes the elasticating teacher
will put things
in the way that
you have to jump
over like the Box.

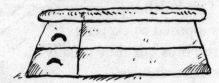

But the AWFUL TRUTH about the Box is that
it suddenly grows taller as you get near it.

It will then punch you in the stomach . . .

. . . or it will trip you up.

Pupils tend to make piles on either side of the Box.

At the end of the elastication lesson, the teacher tests the pupils to make sure they are stretchy and bendy.

If they can't be tied in a knot, they are not properly elasticated.

Mrs Meggabight has now put on her life-jacket and bathing hat. She is going to find out the AWFUL TRUTH about swimming.

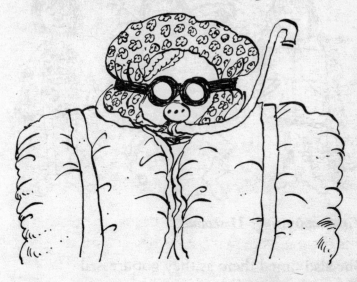

Miss Teylfeather has also prepared herself for taking her class to the swimming pool.

Mrs Meggabight timed the pupils as they got undressed for swimming.

Time undressing: 31 seconds.

She also timed them as they got dressed after swimming.

Time dressing: 31 minutes.

It could be that pupils don't want to go back to school but the really AWFUL TRUTH about swimming is that the pupils' bodies get waterlogged which makes them very slow until they dry out properly.

THE FLYING FISH

THE PENGUINS

THE STARFISH

THE SHARK

THE WHALE

THE ELECTRIC EEL

THE SHIPWRECK

THE HALIBUT →

THE
SEA WEED

THE
CRAB

THE SEAGULL

THE NERVOUS
BREAKDOWN

POOL
ATTENDANT

THE
BARNACLE

THE TIDAL WAVE

THE SEAL

THE JELLYFISH

THE OCTOPUS

THE DOLPHINS

THE
SYNCHRONIZED
MERMAIDS

THE
THING
FROM THE DEEP.

THE TREASURE

Here are some of the other things Mrs Meggabight noticed at the swimming pool . . .

Some pupils took very big bags to the swimming-pool. These were to hold all the things they needed.

Some boys put on boxer shorts to go into the swimming pool but they forgot one important fact . . .

The AWFUL TRUTH about boxer shorts is that they get lost *very easily*.

MEGGABIGHT REPORT ON...
THE AWFUL TRUTH ABOUT TEACHER TANTRUMS

Mrs Meggabight has been measuring teachers' bad moods with her Tantrum Meter.

VOLCANIC ERUPTION

STEAM FROM EARS

SHARP BARK

TUT-TUT!

TIGHT LIPS

STERN LOOK

Here are some of the things she found made
Miss Teylfeather have tantrums:

**The little bit
of paper under
one leg of the
table nearest
the door**

This stops the table from wobbling. If the piece
of paper isn't there then everything zooms onto
the floor.

This made Miss Teylfeather annoyed.

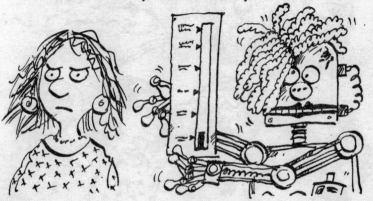

Untidy Jotters

Teachers like jotters to be kept neat and clean. The AWFUL TRUTH about jotters is that they lead very dangerous and exciting lives.

THEY GET STUFFED INTO SCHOOLBAGS

THEY FALL OUT OF CARS →

THEY GET USED AS TABLE MATS

THEY PRETEND TO BE UMBRELLAS →

THWACK!

THEY GET USED AS WEAPONS

DOGS CHEW THEM

What is *this*?

Cardboard Tubes

Cardboard tubes are used for making models.

They are not
to be used by
silly boys
pretending to
be insects.

Pencil Shavings

Pencil shavings all
around the bin but
not in it can
lead to tantrums.
Pupils who can't
aim properly with
their sharpener
are very annoying.

Untidy Lines

All teachers expect pupils to stand in straight, tidy lines.

But the AWFUL TRUTH is that pupils are made of very springy stuff that can't be controlled.

Being very helpful

You would think that Miss Teylfeather would be pleased with helpful pupils.

The AWFUL TRUTH is that great helpfulness can lead to great volcanic eruptions.

THE "AWFUL" "TRUTH" ABOUT SCHOOL DINNERS

Mrs Meggabight has been very brave. She has gone into the dinner hall to gather some facts.

Firstly, Mrs Meggabight found that pupils played a strange game. It was a bit like musical chairs. It was called Find-a-pal-in-the-dinner-queue. It went like this:

Josie saw her pal Zita so she went to join her.

Melanie is Josie's best friend so *she* goes to join *her*.

Then Karen and Janine see their friend Melanie.

Then the teacher shouts **STAND STILL!** All the pupils must stand still for at least three seconds.

Then the game continues. Tommy sees his friend Mark and goes to join *him*. (Tommy hasn't got the hang of the rules of this game yet.)

This game gives pupils a good appetite.
The first one at the front of the queue when the shutters open gets to choose the best food first.

But what exactly goes on behind these kitchen shutters?

Mrs Meggabight went to meet the dinner ladies. She found out the AWFUL TRUTH about the noise behind the shutters.

Mrs Meggabight went into the dinner hall to look at the food for herself. She found lots of food.

FOOD ON THE CEILINGS

FOOD ON WINDOWS

FOOD ON WALLS

SPLAT!

FOOD ON DOORS (IF THE DOORS HAD BEEN SHUT)

FLORENCE

FOOD ON SHOES

FOOD ON FLOORS

The AWFUL TRUTH is that the pupils had no idea whatsoever where their mouths were and very little food went into them.

MEGGABIGHT REPORT ON...

THE AWFUL TRUTH ABOUT LOST THINGS

Mrs Meggabight has found another
AWFUL TRUTH:
lots of things get lost in school. Here are one
or two things that often get lost . . .

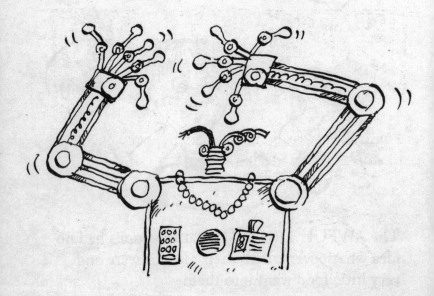

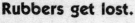

Rubbers get lost.

Rubbers are *always* getting lost.

Please, Miss, I've lost my rubber!

Pupils spend a lot of time wandering round the classroom looking for lost rubbers.

That's my rubber!

Pupils should really tie rubbers to leads, like dogs, to stop them wandering off.

Scissors get lost.

Often this can lead to teacher tantrums.

Time gets lost.

Scissors have a habit of running off on their pointy legs. Pupils then have to lose time looking for lost scissors.

Gloves get lost.

Gloves get lost and they get found.
Children lose gloves . . .

. . . and Mr Glaggum finds gloves. He has a box of 31 gloves in his little room. The strange thing is, the gloves he finds never match the gloves that get lost.

Toilets get lost.

Mrs Meggabight isn't sure if it's the pupil who gets lost on the way to the toilet or if it's the toilet that gets lost.

The AWFUL TRUTH is that the pupil will go and seach for the toilets and not be seen again for *hours*.

Letters that should come and letters that should go get lost.

Pupils often have another job – they act as posties. They have to take letters home from school . . .

. . . and they have to bring letters to school from home.

Cloaks get lost.

Mrs Meggabight has never found any cloaks in the cloakroom. Obviously, pupils are always losing their cloaks.

Lessons get lost.

Teachers give pupils lots of lessons but unless the pupils wear special ear-plugs, the lessons go in one ear and out the other.

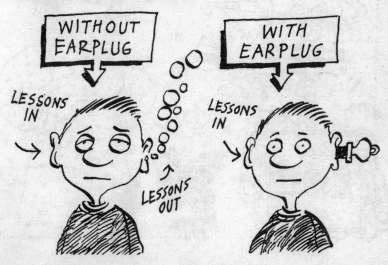

MEGGABIGHT REPORT ON...
THE "AWFUL-TRUTH" ABOUT "EXCUSES"

Mrs Meggabight has realized that pupils are always trying to impress their teachers with excuses. She's been listening in to some of their best excuses.

| ★ ONE STAR EXCUSES | ★★ TWO STAR EXCUSES | ★★★ THREE STAR EXCUSES |

Excuses for not being in your seat

I was only borrowing Catherine's rubber.

I was only looking at Nick's pencil-case.

I was only test-driving my new shoes!

Excuses for not working

 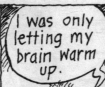 

My pencil's broken.

I was only letting my brain warm up.

A spider was sitting in the middle of my jotter.

Excuses for talking

I was only asking Louise what she got for her birthday.

I wasn't talking!

I was only checking that my voice still worked.

Sometimes the whole class makes an excuse.

Mrs Meggabight found that sometimes, really serious excuses had to be given only to the head teacher. Pupils have to wait in a special waiting-room if they wanted to do this.

The waiting-room is outside the head teacher's office. It's usually between the plant and the display cabinet.

Often, pupils have to wait ages to give their excuse.

When the head teacher calls pupils in, they have to stand on the excuse-giving spot just in front of the head teacher's desk.

The head teacher will ask a question . . .

> I hope you've got a really good excuse for being late every day this week!

Then the pupil will give the excuse . . .

> On Monday, Mum put my trousers in the wash and I had to wait for them to dry.

> On Tuesday, the lollipop lady had a cold and she had to go and buy some tissues and I had to wait until she came back.

> On Wednesday, the traffic lights at the junction were stuck on red and I couldn't cross the road.

> On Thursday, bandits broke into my bedroom, tied me to the bed and stole my school-bag.

Sometimes there are double, treble, or even quadruple excuses.

The AWFUL TRUTH is that pupils are absolutely, totally brilliant at making up excuses and should be given an Oscar.

MEGGABIGHT REPORT ON...

THE 'AWFUL' 'TRUTH' ABOUT "THE SCHOOL PLAY

Mrs Meggabight is taking part in the school play. She's got a copy of the script but the AWFUL TRUTH is, the pupils seem to be doing a completely different play.

PETER AND THE WOLF

CAST LIST
PETER
GRANDFATHER
CAT
BIRD
DUCK
WOLF
HUNTERS
MOON
TREES
FOREST ANIMALS
MUSICIANS

The chorus of forest animals won't stay in their costumes.

The band of recorders and ocarinas won't stay in tune.

The moon has lost her moon.

Grandfather has lost his way.

The cat has lost her temper.

The scenery is behaving strangely.

The bird is behaving like a chicken.

The wolf is behaving badly.

The hunters are playing football with the moon.

Peter is playing truant.

The trees are playing up.

But it will be all right on the night.

MEGGABIGHT REPORT ON...

THE AWFUL TRUTH ABOUT CLEANING LADIES

The cleaning ladies arrive when everyone else is going home. Mrs Meggabight has stayed behind to find out the AWFUL TRUTH about what goes on in school after school.

First of all, the cleaning ladies catch up with the gossip as they fetch their brushes, mops, cloths and buckets.

Then they put a video in the video and switch on the T.V.

Then they start their Aerobic Dusting.

Then they put on
their roller-blades . . .

. . . and they play Sweeping Hockey.

They play Litter Lunge.

In the school hall they play Cobweb Clash.

They play Wheelie Bin Bash.

Then they put on their coats and go home.

MEGGABIGHT REPORT ON...

THE AWFUL TRUTH ABOUT SCHOOL PHOTOGRAPHS

Mrs Meggabight is tidying herself up for the end-of-term photograph.

The photographer has to get the pupils to sit right.

. . . and to sit still . . .

. . . and to smile nicely.

But the AWFUL TRUTH is: *Mission Impossible!*

MEGGABIGHT FINAL REPORT...
THE AWFUL TRUTH ABOUT SCHOOL

Mrs Meggabight has decided that going to school is like going to another planet . . .